Everyday Blessings

Story by Rachael Sands and James Thiemann

Illustrations by Brian Schmidt

"Let all that you do, be done in love."
1 Corinthians 16:14

Illustrations, book design, and typesetting by Brian Schmidt
www.BrianSchmidtArtist.com

ISBN 13: 978-1-64343-764-4
Library of Congress Catalog Number: 2021925222
Printed in the United States
First Printing: 2022
26 25 24 23 22   5 4 3 2 1

Beaver's Pond Press
939 Seventh Street West
Saint Paul, MN 55102
(952) 829-8818
www.BeaversPondPress.com

Find us on Facebook and Instagram at #everydayblessings247

To our little love, Gracey

The pockets in this book are designed to be filled by YOU!
Write notes, draw pictures—express the blessings that feel true!
Find the rainbow pages, connect their edges with tape or glue,
and make a blessings pocket—there are more than one or two!
Let this book of everyday blessings become a part of YOU!

LAKE

In your pockets you will find
little blessings of all kinds.
You may use them every day
to make a difference and find your way.

Great things will come to those who mind
a heart of gratitude for all kinds.
These everyday blessings should find rest—
in your pockets *and* your heart—so you can be your best!

The blessing of wonder
will get you thinking of some things to ponder.
How seeds grow into flowers is a magical thought,
and the power behind this magic is not something to be bought.
It will always be a mystery,
so keep in your pocket a little bit of **curiosity**.

Tape the edges of these rainbow pages together to make a pocket.

Tape the edges of these rainbow pages together to make a pocket.

Always remember that the blessing of **adventure** awaits,
so open your sails and fish with lots of bait.
The mountains you can climb and the paths you can take—
a life full of adventure is truly yours to make.

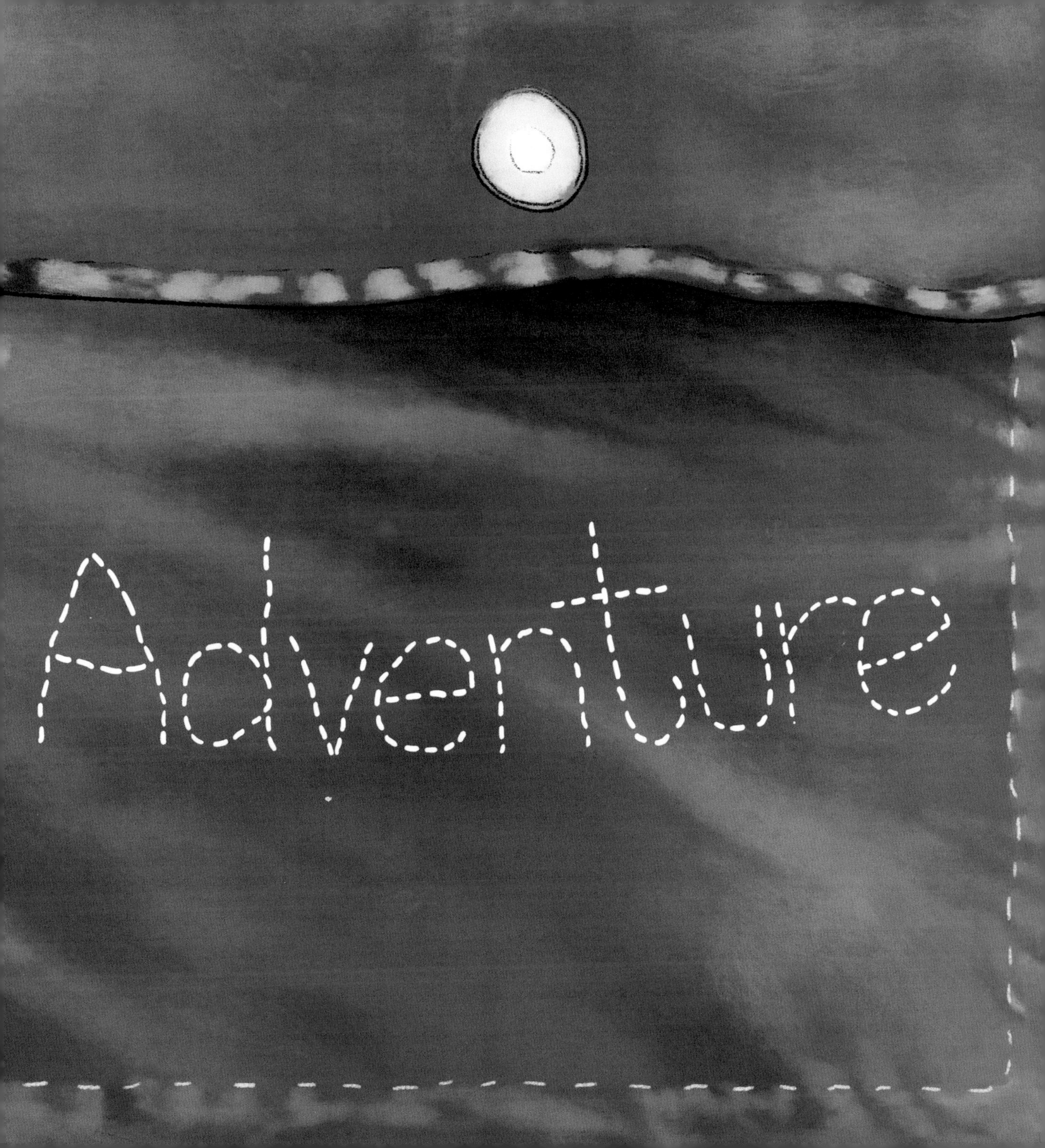
Adventure

Tape the edges of these rainbow pages together to make a pocket.

Tape the edges of these rainbow pages together to make a pocket.

Tape the edges of these rainbow pages together to make a pocket.

There is a **joy** found down in your heart
that will make you smile when no one is about.
This blessing is here for you to feel,
an endless happiness that is so real!

Tape the edges of these rainbow pages together to make a pocket.

Tape the edges of these rainbow pages together to make a pocket.

Tape the edges of these rainbow pages together to make a pocket.

When the sun sets to end a beautiful day—
never forget to be thankful and say,
"When you rise back up, I will too,
sharing my love from me to you."
This blessing is here for you to take
the chance to enjoy the **sunshine** in the moments you make.

Tape the edges of these rainbow pages together to make a pocket.

Tape the edges of these rainbow pages together to make a pocket.

From the depths of the ocean to the sun in the sky,
love gives you a momentum that can make you fly.
Love is breath in our lungs and the beating of our heart.
No matter where you are, this blessing is a form of human art!

Tape the edges of these rainbow pages together to make a pocket.

Tape the edges of these rainbow pages together to make a pocket.

No matter how big or how small,
this blessing of **courage** will be most challenging of all.
It takes a great strength to stand up for what is right,
because times will be hard, and patience will be tight.
This bravery of spirit, you see,
will give strength and hope to you and to me.

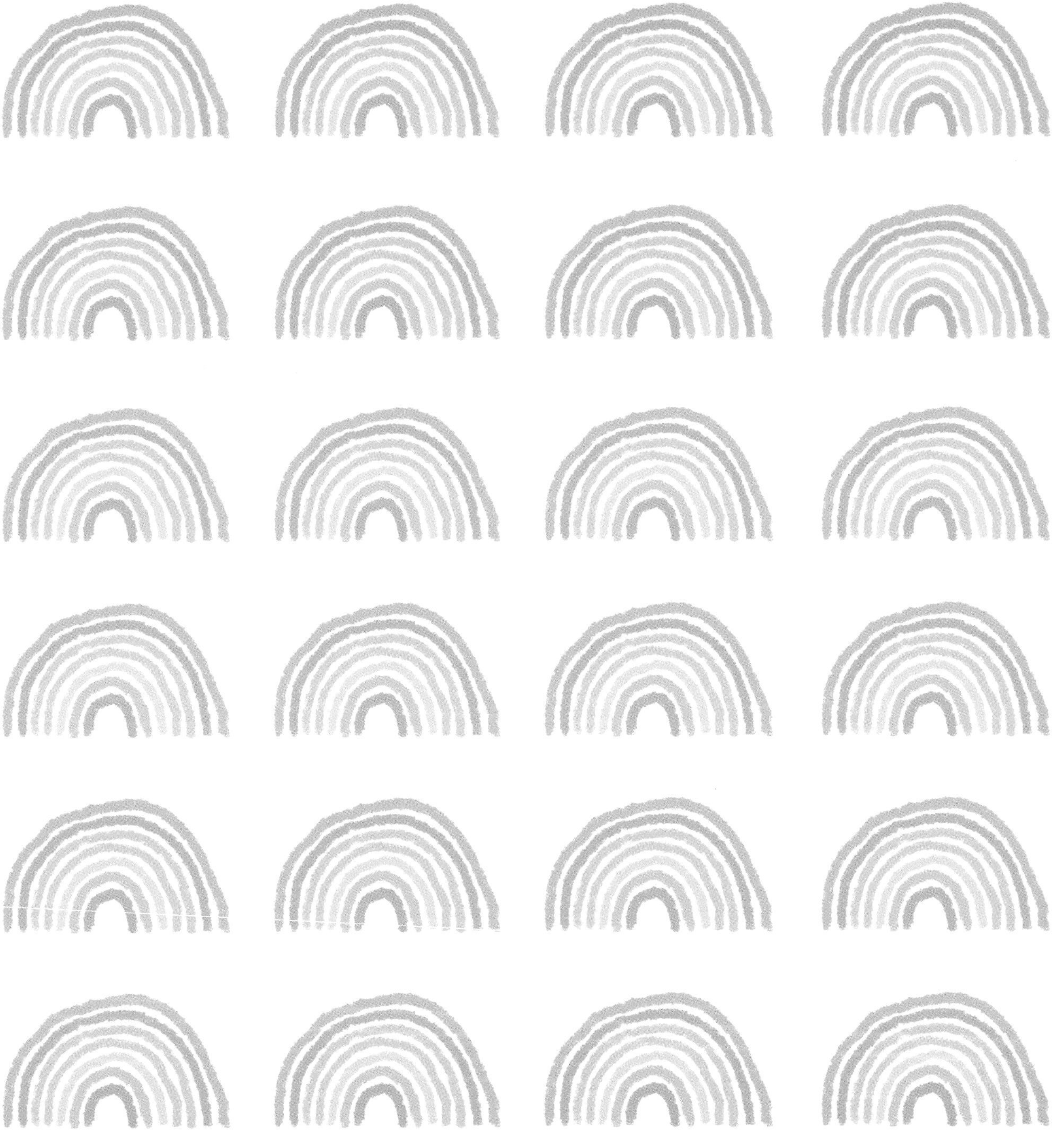

Tape the edges of these rainbow pages together to make a pocket.

How can we believe in something we cannot see?
Well, the blessing of **faith** is for us to be free.
What do you wish for and what do you dream?
These questions can be answered by something unseen.
Faith will be helpful during the very hard times
when you don't have the answers and need to unwind.

Faith

Tape the edges of these rainbow pages together to make a pocket.

Tape the edges of these rainbow pages together to make a pocket.

Tape the edges of these rainbow pages together to make a pocket.

There will be times when you argue and fight,
but **kindness** is key to making things right.
Your gentleness toward people, you know,
will bring peace to your heart and help others grow!
This blessing you will pass along
when you make it a part of your very own song.

Tape the edges of these rainbow pages together to make a pocket.

Tape the edges of these rainbow pages together to make a pocket.

Tape the edges of these rainbow pages together to make a pocket.

When you use these pockets, it's true,
you'll find the person inside who is you!
You are uniquely designed, inside and out,
so let yourself shine—laugh, sing, and shout!
Be true to yourself—that is what you should do.
And use these blessings to become the best version of you!

Tape the edges of these rainbow pages together to make a pocket.

Tape the edges of these rainbow pages together to make a pocket.

Everyday Blessings is our way of sharing and reflecting on our heart of gratitude. We started by posting simple blessings to be thankful for each day, and it grew into something we wanted to share as a legacy for all children and families. Together we have faced many trials and tribulations, as James has a miraculous testimony. Our faith has truly stuck with us, and each of these blessings has brought us a true understanding of our purpose. We hope this book brings peace to your home and joy to your heart!

Blessings always,
Rachael & James